This Coloring Book Belongs To

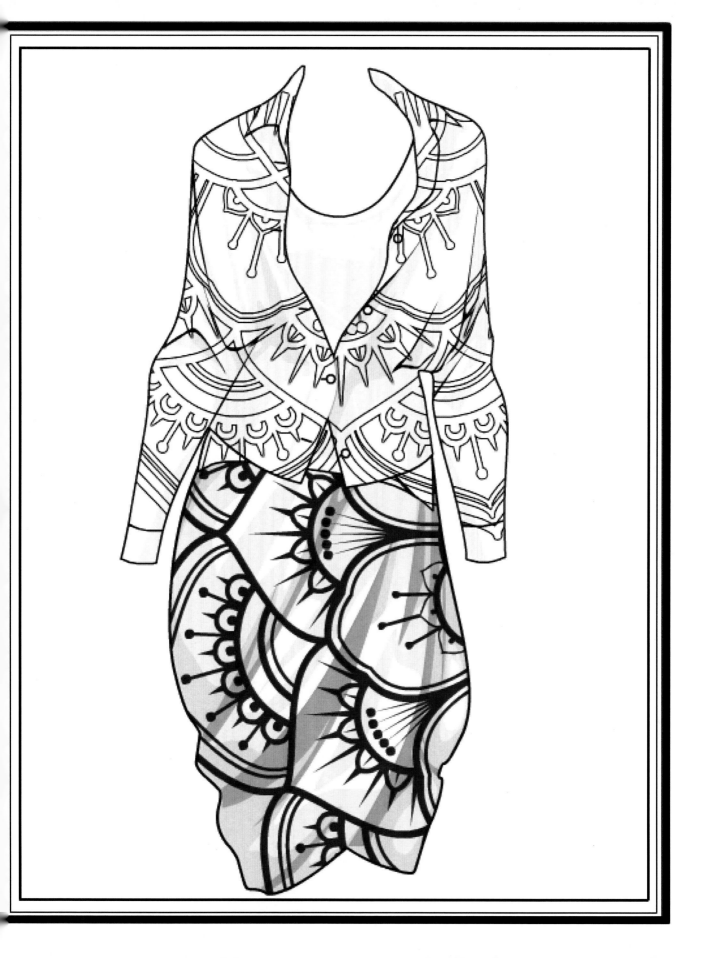

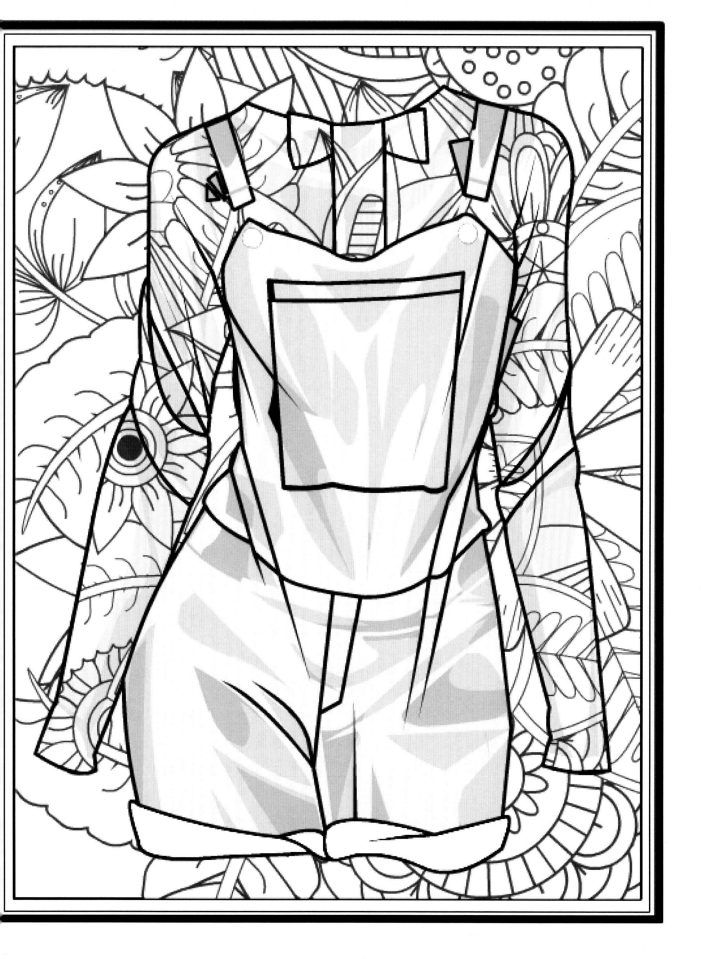

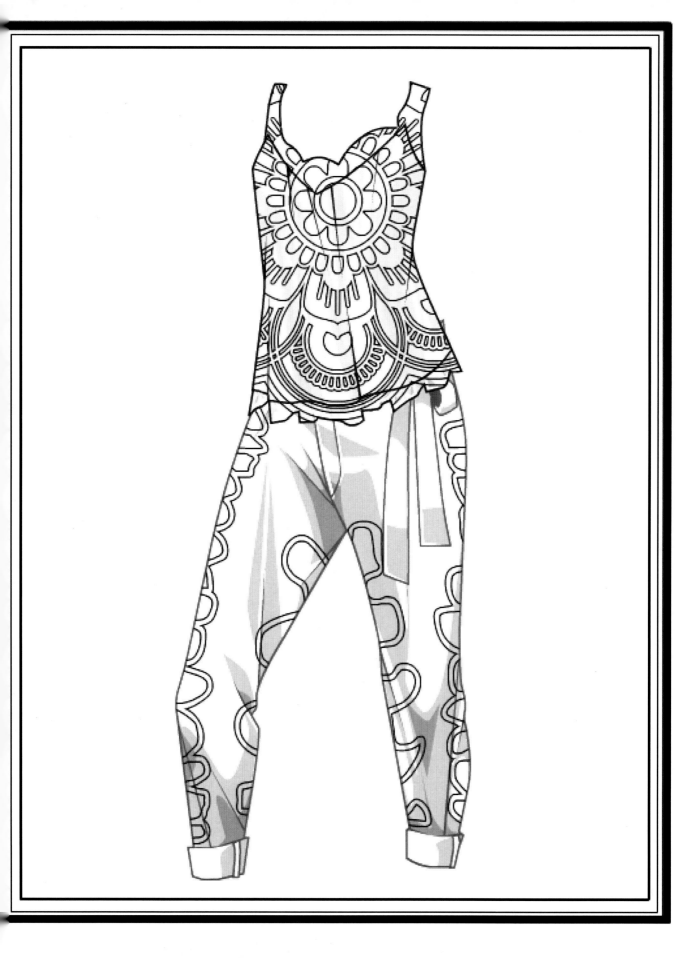

A thousand thanks for purchasing this book. We really appreciate. We are a small family company and thanks to you, we can exist.

We are young, but we have big hearts and we do our best to offer you the **HIGHEST QUALITY** books to enjoy coloring. If you like coloring our book, we have a very modest request: **PLEASE**, take a few seconds of your time to leave us a review on this book's Amazon product page.

You can't imagine how pleased we are for your support and we are doing our best to deliver you the best books. We wish you only the best and if you want to reach us for any inquiries, please send an email at

acriscoloringbook@gmail.com

Thanks for your purchase !
Enjoy coloring !

Made in United States
North Haven, CT
05 August 2022